This book belongs to

....

....

....

For my Mum –

Who taught me the true meaning of love

Hickman and Rye Publishing
Text © Claire Peters 2019
Illustrations © Claire Peters 2019

ISBN: 978-1-9161945-3-3

The
Christmas Gift

Claire Peters

 Find the sparkles hidden on the pages

There's a special something
that's all around

It's everywhere if you look
really carefully

It's outside living in the trees as they swish and sway

And in the teenie, tiny ants as they carry the huge leaves

It's in the scorching, smiling sun

And the shimmering, shiny moon

It's when
opening the
window to let the
beautiful
butterfly out

It's stroking and helping a poorly kitten
at the side of the road

It's in the extra big step taken
to avoid squishing the snail

It's collecting an old colourful
balloon floating in the sea

It's helping the teacher give out
text books to the class

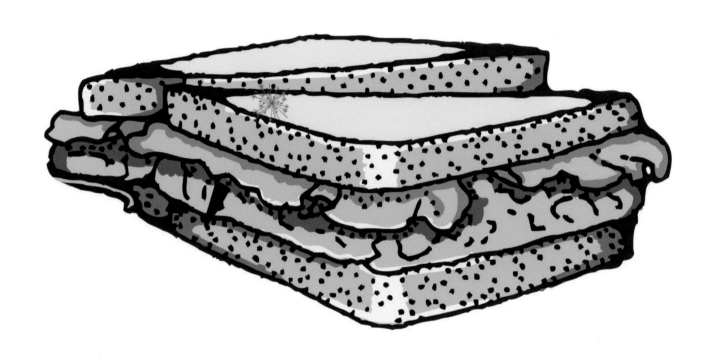

It's sharing your sandwich with a friend who forgot their lunch

It's rescuing a bee drowning in a swimming pool

It's the feeling when you have found
the missing puzzle piece

It's drawing a special picture for
Grandma and Grandpa

It's like the wind...

It's like the sun...

It's an energy and a feeling,
combined as one

It's felt very strongly at Christmas time

We feel it and we see it

But really it's here all year round

What is this Christmas gift we see every day?

It is the gift of Love...

CHRISTMAS PUZZLES

Can you help Max the mouse find the Christmas pudding. He is very hungry...

How many sparkles can you find in this picture of Bentley and Otto?
Look carefully, they are hard to find!

Can you colour in this Christmas bauble so that it is pretty for the
Christmas tree?

About the Author

Claire Peters lives on a farm in East Sussex. She is married to Andrew, and they have two teenage children.

They share their home with Bentley, Otto, a cat called Tobi, and lots of chickens and small animals, including Frank the little tortoise.

Claire has always enjoyed writing poems and stories for her two children when they were young.

We can all name our favourite books we had as children. Claire truly believes that capturing our children's imagination with books, starts from the moment they are born. Whether it is in rhyme, song or spoken word.

The Christmas Gift is Claire's fifth book.

Discover...

The Adventures of Bentley, Otto and Bob

The Adventures of Bentley, Otto and Bob stories feature Bentley the Boxer dog and Otto the Hungarian Vizsla, who have lots of fun adventures! Each story is told through the eyes of Bob the flea, who is kind and very wise. Bob the flea is always with Bentley and Otto, and is able to jump between the two, as and when he likes! He is totally immune to any form of flea treatment...

The stories are fun and rhythmical with an underlying message; such as the importance of friendship, love and kindness. All important qualities to teach our children.

The Adventures of Bentley, Otto and Bob are enjoyed by adults and children alike, and they will transport your children into a World full of fun, mischief, love and laughter!

Discover the world of Bentley, Otto and Bob...

Did you find the sparkles hidden in the
pictures?
How many did you find?

Printed in Poland
by Amazon Fulfillment
Poland Sp. z o.o., Wrocław

51767506R00021